IMAGINE THAT™

Licensed exclusively to Imagine That Publishing Ltd
Tide Mill Way, Woodbridge, Suffolk, IP12 1AP, UK
www.imaginethat.com
Copyright © 2019 Imagine That Group Ltd
All rights reserved
4 6 8 9 7 5 3
Manufactured in China

Written by Joshua George
Illustrated by Gail Yerrill

ISBN 978-1-78958-302-1

A catalogue record for this book is available from the British Library

I Love My Daddy

Written by Joshua George   Illustrated by Gail Yerrill

I love my daddy because …
he gives me a cuddle every morning.

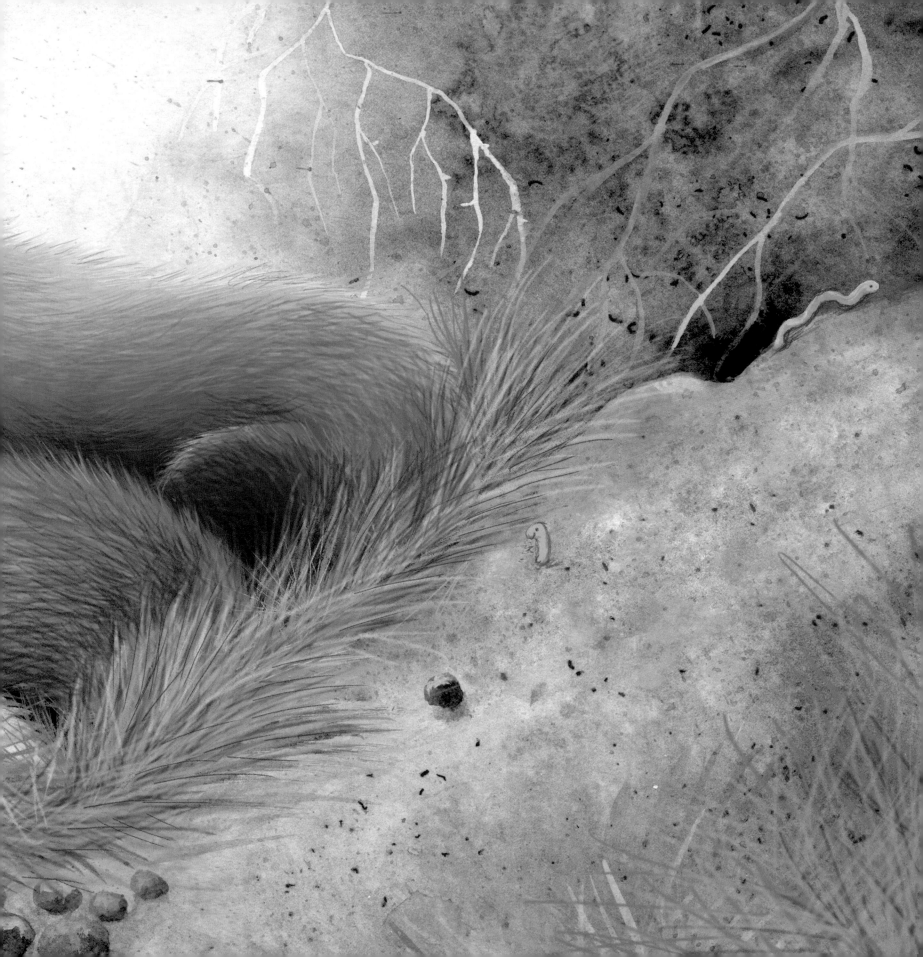

I love my daddy because …
he gets me my favourite breakfast.

I love my daddy because ...
he knows a lot of things.

I love my daddy because …
he doesn't mind if I get dirty.

I love my daddy because ...
he is always ready to play.

I love my daddy because ...
he takes me on adventures.

I love my daddy because ...
he is nice to mummy.

I love my daddy because ...
he is warm and cosy.

I love my daddy because …
he plays with me at bath time.

I love my daddy because ...
he looks after me.

I love my daddy because …

my daddy loves me.